# Table of Contents

MW00605667

# 6 Important Nutrients

> **Directions:** Read about your assigned nutrient and then fill in the template for that nutrient, using the information you learned. Fill in the template for the other nutrients as the other members of your group report.

## Nutrient ① Carbohydrates

**The Good News**
(what this nutrient does for your body)

_____

_____

**The Bad News**
(what happens if you get too much or too little of this nutrient)

_____

_____

**Come and Get It** (what are some foods that are good sources of this nutrient)

_____

**Bottom Line** Eating the right amount of this nutrient is important because...

_____

## Nutrient ② Fats

**The Good News**
(what this nutrient does for your body)

_____

_____

**The Bad News**
(what happens if you get too much or too little of this nutrient)

_____

_____

**Come and Get It** (what are some foods that are good sources of this nutrient)

_____

**Bottom Line** Eating the right amount of this nutrient is important because...

_____

## Nutrient ③ Protein

**The Good News**
(what this nutrient does for your body)

_____

_____

**The Bad News**
(what happens if you get too much or too little of this nutrient)

_____

_____

**Come and Get It** (what are some foods that are good sources of this nutrient)

_____

**Bottom Line** Eating the right amount of this nutrient is important because...

_____

# 6 Important Nutrients *(continued)*

## Nutrient ④ Vitamins

**The Good News**
(what this nutrient does for your body)

**The Bad News**
(what happens if you get too much or too little of this nutrient)

_____

_____

_____

_____

**Come and Get It** (what are some foods that are good sources of this nutrient)

_____

**Bottom Line** Eating the right amount of this nutrient is important because...

_____

## Nutrient ⑤ Minerals

**The Good News**
(what this nutrient does for your body)

**The Bad News**
(what happens if you get too much or too little of this nutrient)

_____

_____

_____

_____

**Come and Get It** (what are some foods that are good sources of this nutrient)

_____

**Bottom Line** Eating the right amount of this nutrient is important because...

_____

## Nutrient ⑥ Water

**The Good News**
(what this nutrient does for your body)

**The Bad News**
(what happens if you get too much or too little of this nutrient)

_____

_____

_____

_____

**Come and Get It** (what are some foods that are good sources of this nutrient)

_____

**Bottom Line** Eating the right amount of this nutrient is important because...

_____

# All About Nutrients

> **Directions:** Think about what you learned from the group presentations on nutrients. Then complete the information for each nutrient by listing at least 2 foods you enjoy that are good sources and explaining at least 1 benefit you get from eating the right amount of this nutrient. Then answer the question.

## ▶ Carbohydrates

Some foods I enjoy that are good sources of carbohydrates:

_____

_____

Making sure I get the right amount of carbohydrates is important because:

_____

_____

_____

## ▶ Fats

Some foods I enjoy that are good sources of fats:

_____

_____

Making sure I get the right amount of fats is important because:

_____

_____

_____

## ▶ Proteins

Some foods I enjoy that are good sources of proteins:

_____

_____

Making sure I get the right amount of protein is important because:

_____

_____

_____

# All About Nutrients *(continued)*

## ▶ Vitamins

Some foods I enjoy that are good sources of vitamins:

_____

_____

Making sure I get the right amount of vitamins is important because:

_____

_____

_____

## ▶ Minerals

Some foods I enjoy that are good sources of minerals:

_____

_____

Making sure I get the right amount of minerals is important because:

_____

_____

_____

## ▶ Water

Some foods and beverages I enjoy that are good sources of water:

_____

_____

Making sure I get the right amount of water is important because:

_____

_____

_____

How is a person's nutrition related to his or her overall health? Give at least 1 example of how a healthy diet can contribute to good health.

_____

_____

_____

**Self-Check**
- ☐ I listed at least 2 foods for each nutrient.
- ☐ I explained at least 1 benefit from eating the right amount of each nutrient.
- ☐ I explained how nutrition is related to overall health and gave at least 1 example.

# Dietary Guidelines: How Am I Doing?

> **Directions:** Think about your eating habits and rate how well you follow the 6 dietary guidelines. Explain what you're already doing to follow each guideline and at least 2 things you could do to improve. Then answer the questions.

| ▶ **Guidelines** | I do this every day. | I do this on most days of the week. | I do this once in a while. | I rarely follow this guideline. |
|---|---|---|---|---|
| **1 Make half your plate fruits and vegetables.** | Excellent ☐ | Good ☐ | Fair ☐ | Poor ☐ |

What I do to follow this guideline: _____

What I could do to improve: _____

| | I do this every day. | I do this on most days of the week. | I do this once in a while. | I rarely follow this guideline. |
|---|---|---|---|---|
| **2 Make at least half your grains whole grains.** | Excellent ☐ | Good ☐ | Fair ☐ | Poor ☐ |

What I do to follow this guideline: _____

What I could do to improve: _____

| | | | | |
|---|---|---|---|---|
| **3 Eat less fat.** | Excellent ☐ | Good ☐ | Fair ☐ | Poor ☐ |

What I do to follow this guideline: _____

What I could do to improve: _____

| | | | | |
|---|---|---|---|---|
| **4 Eat less sugar.** | Excellent ☐ | Good ☐ | Fair ☐ | Poor ☐ |

What I do to follow this guideline: _____

What I could do to improve: _____

| | | | | |
|---|---|---|---|---|
| **5 Eat less salt.** | Excellent ☐ | Good ☐ | Fair ☐ | Poor ☐ |

What I do to follow this guideline: _____

What I could do to improve: _____

| | | | | |
|---|---|---|---|---|
| **6 Balance calories to stay at a healthy weight.** | Excellent ☐ | Good ☐ | Fair ☐ | Poor ☐ |

What I do to follow this guideline: _____

What I could do to improve: _____

# Dietary Guidelines: How Am I Doing?

*(continued)*

## ▶ Questions

**①** Explain in your own words how each of the dietary guidelines can help you plan to eat healthy. Give at least 2 examples of how you would apply each guideline.

_____

_____

_____

_____

_____

_____

_____

_____

_____

_____

_____

_____

_____

_____

**②** Describe why it's important to eat healthy, balance calories and be physically active to maintain a healthy weight.

_____

_____

_____

_____

_____

_____

_____

_____

_____

_____

### Self-Check

☐ I rated how well I follow the 6 dietary guidelines.

☐ I explained what I am doing to follow each guideline and listed at least 2 things I could do to improve.

☐ I explained how the guidelines can be used to help me plan to eat healthy and gave at least 2 examples.

☐ I explained why eating healthy, balancing calories and being physically active are important to stay at a healthy weight.

# Food Log

> **Directions:** List everything you eat and drink over the next 24 hours. Write down the food and beverages you have for each meal and as between-meal snacks, and how much of each one you eat or drink (for example, 1 piece, 1 cup, 16 ounces).

| Time | Food/Beverage | Amount |
|---|---|---|
| **Breakfast** | | |
| | | |
| | | |
| | | |
| **Snacks** | | |
| | | |
| | | |
| | | |
| **Lunch** | | |
| | | |
| | | |
| | | |
| **Snacks** | | |
| | | |
| | | |
| | | |
| **Dinner** | | |
| | | |
| | | |
| | | |
| **Snacks** | | |
| | | |
| | | |

# MyPlate for Teens

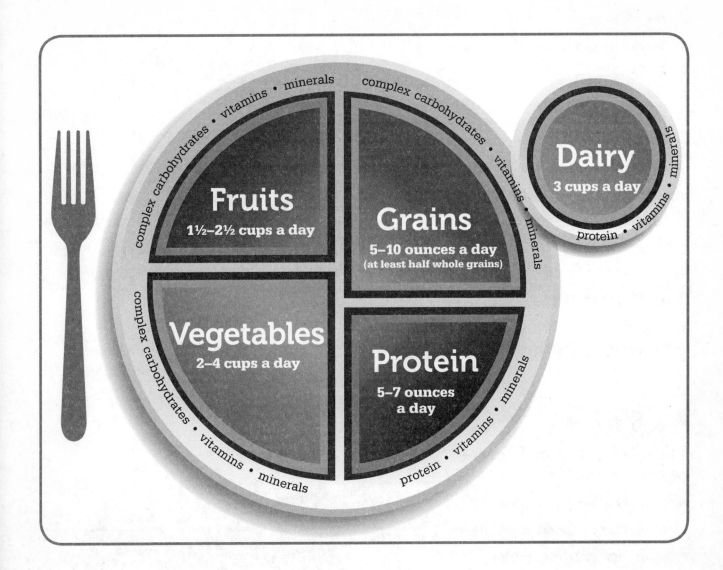

**Fruits**
1½–2½ cups a day

**Grains**
5–10 ounces a day
(at least half whole grains)

**Vegetables**
2–4 cups a day

**Protein**
5–7 ounces
a day

**Dairy**
3 cups a day

complex carbohydrates • vitamins • minerals
complex carbohydrates • vitamins • minerals
complex carbohydrates • vitamins • minerals
protein • vitamins • minerals
protein • vitamins • minerals

# How Much Should I Eat?

## ▶ Grains

**These all count as 1 ounce of grains:**

- 1 slice bread
- ½ hot dog bun or hamburger bun
- ½ small bagel
- ½ English muffin
- 5 whole-wheat crackers
- 6-inch tortilla
- 1 cup cold cereal
- ½ cup cooked cereal
- ½ cup cooked rice
- ½ cup cooked pasta

You need **5–10 ounces** of grains a day.

This is **1 whole** English muffin.
It counts as **2 ounces** of grains.

## ▶ Vegetables

**These all count as ½ cup of vegetables:**

- ½ cup cooked vegetables
- ½ cup raw chopped vegetables
- 1 cup raw leafy vegetables
- ½ cup vegetable juice
- ½ medium baked potato
- ½ cup mashed potatoes
- ½ cup tomato sauce

You need **2–4 cups** of vegetables a day.

This is **½ cup** of cooked vegetables.

# How Much Should I Eat? *(continued)*

## ▶ Fruits

**These all count as ½ cup of fruit:**

- 1 small fruit (apple, orange, pear, peach)
- ½ cup of berries
- ¼ cup dried fruit
- ½ cup canned fruit
- ½ cup 100% fruit juice

You need **1½–2½ cups** of fruit a day.

This is **½ cup** of berries.

## ▶ Dairy

**These all count as 1 cup of dairy:**

- 1 cup (8 ounces) milk or yogurt
- 1½ ounces cheese (or 2 slices)
- 2 cups cottage cheese
- 1 cup frozen yogurt
- 1 cup calcium–fortified soymilk

You need **3 cups** of dairy a day.

This is **1½ ounces** of cheese.
It counts as **1 cup** of dairy.

## ▶ Protein

**These all count as 1 ounce of protein:**

- 1 ounce cooked lean meat, poultry or fish (a small hamburger patty is about 3 ounces)
- 1 egg
- ¼ cup tofu
- ¼ cup cooked beans or peas
- 1 tablespoon peanut butter
- ½ ounce nuts or seeds (12 almonds)

You need **5–7 ounces** of protein foods a day.

This is **½ cup** of cooked beans.
It counts as **2 ounces** of protein.

# What's on MyPlate?

**Directions:** Use what you've learned about MyPlate to plan one day of healthy eating for yourself. First find and circle your calorie level. Then fill out the chart by listing each food and the amount you would eat. Example: 1 cup orange juice. Be sure your totals fit the amounts for the calorie level you've chosen. Then answer the questions.

| Calorie Range | Inactive | Moderately Active | Active |
|---|---|---|---|
| Males 14–18 | 2,000–2,400 | 2,400–2,800 | 2,800–3,200 |
| Females 14–18 | 1,800 | 2,000 | 2,400 |

| Calorie Level | 1,800 | 2,000 | 2,200 | 2,400 | 2,600 | 2,800 | 3,000 | 3,200 |
|---|---|---|---|---|---|---|---|---|
| Grains | 6 oz. | 6 oz. | 7 oz. | 8 oz. | 9 oz. | 10 oz. | 10 oz. | 10 oz. |
| Vegetables | 2.5 cups | 2.5 cups | 3 cups | 3 cups | 3.5 cups | 3.5 cups | 4 cups | 4 cups |
| Fruits | 1.5 cups | 2 cups | 2 cups | 2 cups | 2 cups | 2.5 cups | 2.5 cups | 2.5 cups |
| Dairy | 3 cups | 3 cups | 3 cups | 3 cups | 3 cups | 3 cups | 3 cups | 3 cups |
| Protein | 5 oz. | 5.5 oz. | 6 oz. | 6.5 oz. | 6.5 oz. | 7 oz. | 7 oz. | 7 oz. |

| Food Group | Breakfast | Lunch | Dinner | Snacks | Daily amounts total |
|---|---|---|---|---|---|
| Grains | | | | | |
| Vegetables | | | | | |
| Fruits | | | | | |
| Dairy | | | | | |
| Protein | | | | | |

# What's on MyPlate? *(continued)*

**1** How can eating a variety of foods from each food group help you get the nutrients and calories you need each day? Why is this important?

_____

_____

_____

_____

_____

_____

_____

_____

**2** What are at least 3 benefits of healthy eating?

_____

_____

_____

_____

_____

_____

_____

**3** Which benefit of healthy eating do you think is most important? Explain why. Be specific.

_____

_____

_____

_____

_____

_____

_____

_____

_____

### Self-Check

☐ I met the requirements for all food groups for my calorie and activity levels.

☐ I described how eating a variety of foods from each food group would help me get the nutrients I need and balance calories and explained why this is important.

☐ I described at least 3 benefits of healthy eating and explained which is most important to me and why.

# MyPlate Food Log

> **Directions:** List everything you eat and drink over the next 24 hours. Write down the food and beverages you have for each meal and as between-meal snacks, and how much of each one you eat or drink (for example, 1 piece, 1 cup, 16 ounces). Then check which food group this food or beverage is from.

| Time | Food/Beverage | Amount | Grains | Vegetables | Fruits | Protein | Dairy | Other |
|---|---|---|---|---|---|---|---|---|
| **Breakfast** | | | ☐ | ☐ | ☐ | ☐ | ☐ | ☐ |
| | | | ☐ | ☐ | ☐ | ☐ | ☐ | ☐ |
| | | | ☐ | ☐ | ☐ | ☐ | ☐ | ☐ |
| | | | ☐ | ☐ | ☐ | ☐ | ☐ | ☐ |
| **Snacks** | | | ☐ | ☐ | ☐ | ☐ | ☐ | ☐ |
| | | | ☐ | ☐ | ☐ | ☐ | ☐ | ☐ |
| | | | ☐ | ☐ | ☐ | ☐ | ☐ | ☐ |
| **Lunch** | | | ☐ | ☐ | ☐ | ☐ | ☐ | ☐ |
| | | | ☐ | ☐ | ☐ | ☐ | ☐ | ☐ |
| | | | ☐ | ☐ | ☐ | ☐ | ☐ | ☐ |
| | | | ☐ | ☐ | ☐ | ☐ | ☐ | ☐ |
| **Snacks** | | | ☐ | ☐ | ☐ | ☐ | ☐ | ☐ |
| | | | ☐ | ☐ | ☐ | ☐ | ☐ | ☐ |
| | | | ☐ | ☐ | ☐ | ☐ | ☐ | ☐ |
| **Dinner** | | | ☐ | ☐ | ☐ | ☐ | ☐ | ☐ |
| | | | ☐ | ☐ | ☐ | ☐ | ☐ | ☐ |
| | | | ☐ | ☐ | ☐ | ☐ | ☐ | ☐ |
| | | | ☐ | ☐ | ☐ | ☐ | ☐ | ☐ |
| **Snacks** | | | ☐ | ☐ | ☐ | ☐ | ☐ | ☐ |
| | | | ☐ | ☐ | ☐ | ☐ | ☐ | ☐ |
| | | | ☐ | ☐ | ☐ | ☐ | ☐ | ☐ |

# Food Label Analysis

**Directions:** Answer the questions and compare the food labels on your **Which Food Would You Choose?** sheet.

## ▶ Food Label 1

**1** What's the serving size? _____

**2** How many calories per serving? _____

**3** How many calories per serving come from fat? (1 g fat = 9 calories) _____

**4** How many grams of saturated fat? _____ Trans fat? _____

**5** How many milligrams of cholesterol? _____

**6** How many grams of protein? _____

**7** How many grams of total carbohydrate? _____

**8** How many grams of dietary fiber? _____ Sugars? _____

**9** What percent daily value of each of these nutrients does a serving provide?

Vitamin A _____    Calcium _____    Dietary Fiber _____

Vitamin C _____    Iron _____    Sodium _____

## ▶ Food Label 2

**1** What's the serving size? _____

**2** How many calories per serving? _____

**3** How many calories per serving come from fat? (1 g fat = 9 calories) _____

**4** How many grams of saturated fat? _____ Trans fat? _____

**5** How many milligrams of cholesterol? _____

**6** How many grams of protein? _____

**7** How many grams of total carbohydrate? _____

**8** How many grams of dietary fiber? _____ Sugars? _____

**9** What percent daily value of each of these nutrients does a serving provide?

Vitamin A _____    Calcium _____    Dietary Fiber _____

Vitamin C _____    Iron _____    Sodium _____

Which of these 2 foods is a healthier choice? Why?

_____

_____

_____

_____

### Self-Check
☐ I answered all the questions about both foods.
☐ I stated which food is a healthier choice and explained why.

# Supersizing America

## ▶ Americans like a bargain!

### Marketing experts know it and food producers are delivering.

The fast-food industry is a $110-billion-dollar-a-year business. **Supersizing** is a major strategy used to appeal to Americans' desire to get a deal.

**Supersizing** has contributed to a growing health crisis:

- About 25% of American adults visit a fast-food restaurant every day.

- There's been a dramatic increase in obesity in the United States over the last 20 years.

- More than 68% of adults over age 20 are either overweight or obese. Around 17% of children and teens are obese.

- Obesity-related diseases include heart disease, stroke and diabetes.

- Many food ads focus on fast food, sweetened cereals and candy.

Some facts about **supersizing:**

- **It's a historical trend.** Serving sizes being sold to consumers have increased dramatically over the years. The average-size cola drink in the 1950s was 6.5 oz. (85 calories). Today the average cola drink is 20 oz. (260 calories). Regular-size servings of french fries and hamburgers are more than 2 times larger than in the 1950s.

- **Food companies use larger sizes as selling points.** Fast-food companies promote larger items with TV and radio ads, signs, staff pins, and placemats. Manufacturers of frozen dinners advertise "man size" meals. Restaurant reviewers refer to large portions. Most fast-food restaurants sell french fries in medium, large and supersize.

- **It's not really such a bargain.** Even though supersizing "saves" you money—for example, you might get twice as much soda for only 50 cents more—it costs you in terms of health. For example, if a person drank a 32 oz. cola each day, without increasing his or her physical activity, it would result in a weight gain of over 40 pounds in 1 year.

# Making My Fast-Food Meal Healthier

#### Part 1

**Directions:** Write the name of your favorite fast-food restaurant and list your favorite meal from the restaurant. Be as specific as possible. For example, include the size of the food item (e.g., small, medium, large, super), regular or diet soda, and any condiments that you use (e.g., mayonnaise, ketchup, salad dressing). Then use the menu your teacher gives you to find out how many calories, grams (g) of fat and milligrams (mg) of sodium are in the meal you listed.

**Restaurant** _____

| Menu Item | Calories | Fat | Sodium |
|-----------|----------|-----|--------|
| | | | |
| | | | |
| | | | |
| | | | |
| | | | |
| | | | |

▶ Part 2

**Directions:** Now calculate what percent of the total maximum daily intake of calories, fat and sodium this meal has.

| Total Calories % of daily intake (2,400) | Total Fat % of daily intake (80g) | Total Sodium % of daily intake (2,300) |
|---|---|---|
| | | |

*(continued)*

# Making My Fast-Food Meal Healthier *(continued)*

#### Part 3

> **Directions:** Revise the meal in Part 1 to make it healthier (or create another healthy meal from the menu). Make sure you choose food items that you would really eat when going to the fast-food restaurant. Then answer the questions.

| Menu Item | Calories | Fat | Sodium |
|---|---|---|---|
| _____ | | | |
| _____ | | | |
| _____ | | | |
| _____ | | | |
| _____ | | | |
| _____ | | | |

| Total Calories % of daily intake (2,400) | Total Fat % of daily intake (80g) | Total Sodium % of daily intake (2,300) |
|---|---|---|
| | | |

**1** **What changes did you make to improve your fast-food meal? Be specific.**

_____

_____

_____

_____

**2** **What are at least 3 ways to prepare food so it has less fat, sugar and sodium?**

_____

_____

_____

_____

_____

## Self-Check

☐ I listed my favorite fast-food meal and wrote nutrition facts for each item.

☐ I made changes to make the meal healthier and wrote the nutrition facts that explain how each food is a healthier choice.

☐ I listed at least 3 ways to prepare food so it has less fat, sugar and sodium.

# Activity Log

**Directions:** Keep track of all the physical activity you do over the next 24 hours. Include planned activities and sports, as well as any time you spend walking, riding a bike, climbing stairs, dancing, etc. Describe each activity you do, and be sure to note how long you did the activity (for example, 5 minutes, half hour).

| Time | Activity I did | How long I did this activity |
|------|----------------|------------------------------|
|      |                |                              |
|      |                |                              |
|      |                |                              |
|      |                |                              |
|      |                |                              |
|      |                |                              |
|      |                |                              |
|      |                |                              |
|      |                |                              |

# Sharing Fitness Facts

**Directions:** Suppose you have a friend who's very inactive, but lately has been talking about wanting to become more physically fit. Fill in your part of the conversation to answer your friend's questions about the components of fitness and convince him or her of the benefits of physical activity.

**1** **Your friend says,** "People talk about being fit, but what exactly does that mean?"

**You say:** (Be sure your answer explains the different components of fitness.)

_____

_____

_____

**2** **Your friend says,** "Can't I just lift weights every day to get in shape?"

**You say:** (Be sure your answer explains why it's important to build each of the different components of fitness.)

_____

_____

_____

**3** **Your friend says,** "What kinds of things should I do to get more fit?"

**You say:** (Be sure your answer suggests at least 1 activity for each of the 4 components of fitness.)

_____

_____

_____

**4** **Your friend says,** "So, what will being physically active do for me anyway?"

**You say:** (Be sure your answer describes at least 3 physical and 2 mental and/or social benefits of physical activity.)

_____

_____

_____

_____

## Self-Check

☐ I named all 4 components of fitness and explained the importance of each in my answers.

☐ I listed at least 1 activity for each component.

☐ I described at least 3 physical and 2 mental and/or social benefits of physical activity.

# Physical Activity & Fitness Quiz

**1** What are 4 components of fitness?

_____

_____

_____

**2** Which 2 body systems does cardiorespiratory fitness strengthen?

_____

_____

**3** What are 3 examples of aerobic activities?

_____

_____

_____

**4** For health benefits, teens should do aerobic activities at least _____ times per week.

**5** How do you know an activity is building cardiorespiratory fitness?

_____

_____

_____

_____

**6** What are 3 examples of physical activities that contribute to muscular strength?

_____

_____

_____

**7** What's muscular endurance?

_____

_____

_____

_____

*(continued)*

# Physical Activity & Fitness Quiz (continued)

**8** How many times a week should teens do muscle-strengthening activities? _____

**9** How many times a week should teens do bone-strengthening activities? _____

**10** Bone-strengthening activities help prevent what disease?

_____

**11** Name 3 activities that help strengthen bones and explain how they do this.

_____

_____

_____

_____

_____

_____

**12** What are 2 activities that contribute to flexibility?

_____

_____

**13** Why are activities that increase flexibility important?

_____

_____

**14** What could a person do to be more physically active? Describe at least 3 ways to increase activity and/or decrease inactivity.

_____

_____

_____

_____

_____

_____

**Self-Check**

☐ I answered all the questions about the guidelines for physical activity.

☐ I described at least 3 ways a person could be more physically active.

**HEALTH** *Smart.* High School

# Physical Activity Plan

**Directions:** Make a week-long activity plan that would enable you to meet the guidelines for physical activity.

- Plan a physical activity for each day of the week and note how many minutes you'll do it, the level of intensity, which component of fitness it will build and whether it's bone strengthening.
- As part of your plan, include ways to increase daily physical activity that are simple to do.

Complete the statements that follow the chart to summarize your plan and be sure it meets the guidelines.

| | Physical Activity | Number of Minutes | Intensity | Type of Fitness | |
|---|---|---|---|---|---|
| Monday | | | ☐ easy ☐ moderate ☐ vigorous | ☐ cardiorespiratory (aerobic) ☐ bone strengthening ☐ muscular strength ☐ endurance | ☐ flexibility ☐ health related ☐ skill related |
| Tuesday | | | ☐ easy ☐ moderate ☐ vigorous | ☐ cardiorespiratory (aerobic) ☐ bone strengthening ☐ muscular strength ☐ endurance | ☐ flexibility ☐ health related ☐ skill related |
| Wednesday | | | ☐ easy ☐ moderate ☐ vigorous | ☐ cardiorespiratory (aerobic) ☐ bone strengthening ☐ muscular strength ☐ endurance | ☐ flexibility ☐ health related ☐ skill related |
| Thursday | | | ☐ easy ☐ moderate ☐ vigorous | ☐ cardiorespiratory (aerobic) ☐ bone strengthening ☐ muscular strength ☐ endurance | ☐ flexibility ☐ health related ☐ skill related |
| Friday | | | ☐ easy ☐ moderate ☐ vigorous | ☐ cardiorespiratory (aerobic) ☐ bone strengthening ☐ muscular strength ☐ endurance | ☐ flexibility ☐ health related ☐ skill related |
| Saturday | | | ☐ easy ☐ moderate ☐ vigorous | ☐ cardiorespiratory (aerobic) ☐ bone strengthening ☐ muscular strength ☐ endurance | ☐ flexibility ☐ health related ☐ skill related |
| Sunday | | | ☐ easy ☐ moderate ☐ vigorous | ☐ cardiorespiratory (aerobic) ☐ bone strengthening ☐ muscular strength ☐ endurance | ☐ flexibility ☐ health related ☐ skill related |

*(continued)*

# Physical Activity Plan

*(continued)*

**Other ways to increase daily activity this week:**

_____

_____

_____

**(1)** My plan includes _____ total minutes of aerobic activity for the week.
**Average minutes per day:** _____

**(2)** My plan includes _____ total minutes of vigorous aerobic activity on _____ days.

**(3)** My plan includes muscle-strengthening activities on _____ days.

**(4)** My plan includes bone-strengthening activities on _____ days.

**(5)** My plan includes these activities to build endurance:

_____

_____

_____

**(6)** My plan includes these activities to increase flexibility:

_____

_____

_____

**(7)** My plan includes these ways to increase activity and decrease inactivity
(include at least 3):

_____

_____

_____

_____

_____

### Self-Check
☐ I created a plan that meets all 4 guidelines for physical activity.

☐ I described at least 3 ways to increase physical activity.

☐ I filled in the chart for all days and completed all the statements.

**HEALTH** *Smart.* High School

# My Daily Physical Activity Log

**Directions:** List all of the physical activities you engage in for the next 24 hours and the number of minutes you do each one. Identify the level of intensity (easy, moderate, vigorous), component(s) of fitness the activity builds and whether the activity is bone strengthening. Then complete the statements.

| | Physical Activity | Number of Minutes | Intensity | Type of Fitness |
|---|---|---|---|---|
| **1** | | | ☐ easy ☐ moderate ☐ vigorous | ☐ cardiorespiratory (aerobic) ☐ bone strengthening ☐ flexibility ☐ muscular strength ☐ health related ☐ endurance ☐ skill related |
| **2** | | | ☐ easy ☐ moderate ☐ vigorous | ☐ cardiorespiratory (aerobic) ☐ bone strengthening ☐ flexibility ☐ muscular strength ☐ health related ☐ endurance ☐ skill related |
| **3** | | | ☐ easy ☐ moderate ☐ vigorous | ☐ cardiorespiratory (aerobic) ☐ bone strengthening ☐ flexibility ☐ muscular strength ☐ health related ☐ endurance ☐ skill related |
| **4** | | | ☐ easy ☐ moderate ☐ vigorous | ☐ cardiorespiratory (aerobic) ☐ bone strengthening ☐ flexibility ☐ muscular strength ☐ health related ☐ endurance ☐ skill related |
| **5** | | | ☐ easy ☐ moderate ☐ vigorous | ☐ cardiorespiratory (aerobic) ☐ bone strengthening ☐ flexibility ☐ muscular strength ☐ health related ☐ endurance ☐ skill related |

I did _____ total minutes of aerobic activity.

I did _____ total minutes of vigorous aerobic activity.

I did muscle-strengthening activities.　　　　☐ Yes ☐ No

I did activities that build endurance.　　　　☐ Yes ☐ No

I did activities that increase flexibility.　　　☐ Yes ☐ No

I did bone-strengthening activities.　　　　☐ Yes ☐ No

**Based on my physical activity today, I'll do this type of physical activity tomorrow:**

_____

_____

# Assessing My Eating & Physical Activity Behaviors

> **Directions:** Read each guideline and rate yourself.

## Eating Behaviors

### ▶ Guideline 1

**Make half your plate fruits and vegetables.**

Fruits and vegetables should be key parts of your daily diet. Fruits and vegetables provide vitamins, minerals, complex carbohydrates and fiber.

### ▶ How I'm Doing

☐ **Excellent:** I eat at least 1½–2½ cups of fruit and 2–4 cups of vegetables daily.

☐ **Good:** I eat 1 cup of fruit and 1–2 cups of vegetables daily.

☐ **Fair:** I eat ½ cup of fruit and ½–1 cup of vegetables every day.

☐ **Poor:** I rarely eat fruits and vegetables.

### ▶ Guideline 2

**Make at least half your grains whole grains.**

Whole-grain foods include whole-grain bread, oatmeal, cereal and pasta. These foods provide vitamins, minerals and complex carbohydrates. One ounce of grain is equal to 1 piece of bread, 1 cup of cereal, or ½ cup cooked rice or pasta.

### ▶ How I'm Doing

☐ **Excellent:** I eat 5–10 oz. of grains daily—at least half are whole grain.

☐ **Good:** I eat 5–10 oz. of grains daily—some are whole grain.

☐ **Fair:** I eat 1–4 oz. of grains daily—some are whole grain.

☐ **Poor:** I rarely eat whole-grain foods.

### ▶ Guideline 3

**Eat less fat.**

Teens should get no more than 25–35% of the total calories they eat from fat. Healthy sources include fish, nuts and vegetable oils. Avoid saturated and trans fats.

### ▶ How I'm Doing

☐ **Excellent:** I eat about the right amount of fat from healthy sources.

☐ **Good:** I eat a little too much fat, but usually choose healthy sources.

☐ **Fair:** I eat too much fat from unhealthy sources.

☐ **Poor:** I eat way too much fat from unhealthy sources.

### ▶ Guideline 4

**Eat less added sugar.**

Sugar added to foods in processing contributes to weight gain, tooth decay and certain diseases.

### ▶ How I'm Doing

☐ **Excellent:** I eat very few foods that contain a lot of added sugar.

☐ **Good:** I eat some foods that contain a lot of added sugar.

☐ **Fair:** Every day, some of the foods I eat contain added sugar.

☐ **Poor:** Every day, many of the foods I eat contain added sugar.

# Assessing My Eating & Physical Activity Behaviors

*(continued)*

## ▶ Guideline 5

### Eat less salt.

Snack foods, processed foods and frozen meals often contain high amounts of salt.

## ▶ How I'm Doing

☐ **Excellent:** I rarely salt my foods or eat foods high in salt.

☐ **Good:** I only occasionally salt my foods or eat foods high in salt.

☐ **Fair:** I sometimes salt my foods and eat some foods high in salt.

☐ **Poor:** I usually salt my foods and eat a lot of foods high in salt.

## ▶ Guideline 6

### Balance calories.

When the calories you take in through eating and drinking match the number of calories your body needs to function and be physically active each day you stay at a healthy weight.

## ▶ How I'm Doing

☐ **Excellent:** I rarely eat more calories than my body needs or burns off through physical activity.

☐ **Good:** Once in a while I eat too many calories, but I usually try to be more active to make up for it.

☐ **Fair:** I sometimes eat too many calories and often don't get enough physical activity.

☐ **Poor:** I eat more calories than I need and don't do much physical activity on most days.

**Areas of strength:** _____

_____

_____

_____

**Areas that need improvement:** _____

_____

_____

_____

**Based on this assessment, what eating behavior would I most like to work on?**

_____

_____

_____

_____

*(continued)*

# Assessing My Eating &
# Physical Activity Behaviors

*(continued)*

# Physical Activity Behaviors

## ▶ Guideline 1

**Be physically active for 60 minutes each day.**

This can include active games, chores, work or recreational activities.

## ▶ How I'm Doing

☐ **Excellent:** I spend 60 minutes each day doing things that count as physical activity.

☐ **Good:** I spend 30–60 minutes each day doing things that count as physical activity.

☐ **Fair:** I spend under 30 minutes each day doing things that count as physical activity.

☐ **Poor:** I am not physically active on most days.

## ▶ Guideline 2

**Include vigorous-intensity aerobic activities at least 3 days per week.**

Vigorous activities make your heart beat fast and your lungs work hard.

## ▶ How I'm Doing

☐ **Excellent:** I do vigorous aerobic activities for at least 30 minutes on 3 or more days per week.

☐ **Good:** I do vigorous aerobic activities for at least 30 minutes on 2 days per week.

☐ **Fair:** I do vigorous aerobic activities for at least 30 minutes on 1 day per week.

☐ **Poor:** I rarely do vigorous aerobic activity.

## ▶ Guideline 3

**Do muscle-strengthening activities at least 3 days a week.**

## ▶ How I'm Doing

☐ **Excellent:** I do muscle-strengthening activities on 3 or more days per week.

☐ **Good:** I do muscle-strengthening activities on 2 days per week.

☐ **Fair:** I do muscle-strengthening activities 1 day per week.

☐ **Poor:** I rarely or never do muscle-strengthening activities.

# Assessing My Eating & Physical Activity Behaviors

*(continued)*

▶ **Guideline 4**

Do bone-strengthening activities at least 3 days a week.

▶ **How I'm Doing**

☐ **Excellent:** I do bone-strengthening activities on 3 or more days per week.

☐ **Good:** I do bone-strengthening activities on 2 days per week.

☐ **Fair:** I do bone-strengthening activities 1 day per week.

☐ **Poor:** I rarely or never do bone-strengthening activities.

Areas of strength: _____
_____
_____
_____

Areas that need improvement: _____
_____
_____
_____

Based on this assessment, what physical activity behavior would I most like to work on?
_____
_____
_____
_____

---

**Self-Check**

☐ I rated myself on all 6 healthy eating and all 4 physical activity guidelines.

☐ I identified strengths and areas that need improvement for all guidelines.

☐ I identified the eating and physical activity behaviors I would most like to work on.

# My Healthy Eating or Physical Activity Goal

> **Directions:** Answer the following questions.

**1** My goal for healthy eating or physical activity:

_____

_____

_____

**2** The benefits of reaching my goal (list at least 2):

_____

_____

_____

_____

**3** This goal is important to me because:

_____

_____

_____

_____

_____

**4** Steps I'll take to reach my goal:

- _____
- _____
- _____
- _____
- _____
- _____

# My Healthy Eating or Physical Activity Goal

*(continued)*

**5** **How will I start?**

_____

_____

_____

_____

_____

_____

**6** **Who can help me? (Name at least 1 person.)**

_____

_____

_____

**7** **Possible barriers that could get in the way:**
**(List at least 1 barrier and a way to overcome it.)**

| Barrier | How I could overcome the barrier |
|---|---|
| _____ | _____ |
| _____ | _____ |
| _____ | _____ |
| _____ | _____ |
| _____ | _____ |

**8** **Who's my class partner who'll support me and help me reach my goal?**

_____

my partner's name

---

**Self-Check**

☐ I stated my goal and listed at least 2 benefits of reaching it.

☐ I described why this goal is important to me.

☐ I described the steps I'll take to reach my goal, including how I'll start.

☐ I listed at least 1 barrier and described how I could overcome it.

☐ I wrote who can help me reach my goal, and who my class partner will be.

---

# Physical Activity Goal
## Sample Plan

You've set a goal for healthy eating or physical activity and exercise. Now you have to decide what you have to do to achieve it.

**You'll want to:**

- Identify the benefits of your healthy behavior.

- Identify barriers—things that could get in the way—and take action to solve problems as they come up.

- Get help from others when you need it.

Sometimes you'll want to push yourself. Other times you may want to take it easy. Keeping track of your progress is a great way to keep yourself motivated.

## ▶ Sarah's Goal

**Sarah set a goal to be physically active for more than 30 minutes at least 5 days a week.**

### Monday

I walked to the library and back after school (20 minutes each way).

### Tuesday

Nothing.

### Wednesday

I rode my bike to my friend Isabella's house in the evening and we went for a 30-minute ride together.

### Thursday

I walked the dog in the park in the morning (15 minutes).

### Friday

I went to a dance at the youth center and stayed on the dance floor for nearly 2 hours.

### What I Learned This Week

**Benefits I enjoyed this week:**

I had fun on my bike. I felt good about almost meeting my goal.

**Problems I had and how I solved them:**

I don't always want to exercise, so it helps to walk somewhere I want to go. It was hard to get up early on Thursday, but I'd promised my mom I'd walk the dog that morning. I need to find ways to be active even if there isn't a dance to go to.

**Who helped me with my goal:**

My friends walked to the library with me. My boyfriend likes dancing too.

**What I am going to do toward my goal this weekend:**

Isabella and I are going to go on a bike ride for at least 30 minutes again on Sunday.

# Tracking My Progress

> **Directions:** Write the healthy eating or physical activity goal that you want to achieve. List the steps you took on each day of the week. At the end of the week, answer the questions about what you learned.

**My goal:** _____

_____

| Week 1<br>What I did... | Sunday | Monday | Tuesday |
|---|---|---|---|
| **Wednesday** | **Thursday** | **Friday** | **Saturday** |
| | | | |

| What I learned... | |
|---|---|
| Benefits: | Who helped me: |
| Problems/barriers: | How I dealt with them: |
| What I'm going to do differently next week: | What I'm going to keep doing: |

*(continued)*

# Tracking My Progress *(continued)*

| Week 2 What I did… | Sunday | Monday | Tuesday |
|---|---|---|---|
| | | | |
| Wednesday | Thursday | Friday | Saturday |
| | | | |

### What I learned…

| Benefits: | Who helped me: |
|---|---|
| Problems/barriers: | How I dealt with them: |
| What I'm going to do differently next week: | What I'm going to keep doing: |

| Week 3 What I did… | Sunday | Monday | Tuesday |
|---|---|---|---|
| | | | |
| Wednesday | Thursday | Friday | Saturday |
| | | | |

### What I learned…

| Benefits: | Who helped me: |
|---|---|
| Problems/barriers: | How I dealt with them: |
| What I'm going to do differently next week: | What I'm going to keep doing: |

**HEALTH** *Smart.* High School

# Succeeding at Fitness

▶ **Part 1**

**Directions:** Using what you've learned, answer the questions.

① Why is it important to drink enough water before, during and after physical activity?

_____

_____

_____

② Explain at least 3 different ways to reduce the risk of injury during physical activity.

_____

_____

_____

③ Describe at least 3 ways you can respond to climate- or weather-related conditions during sports or physical activity.

_____

_____

_____

④ Why is it important to warm up before and cool down after physical activity?

_____

_____

_____

⑤ List at least 3 activities that require safety equipment and explain why it's important to wear safety gear for these activities.

| Activity | Safety Gear Needed | How Gear Will Protect You |
|---|---|---|
| _____ | _____ | _____ |
| _____ | _____ | _____ |
| _____ | _____ | _____ |

⑥ What advice would you give someone who's just beginning to be physically active?

_____

_____

_____

*(continued)*

Nutrition & Physical Activity

# Succeeding at Fitness *(continued)*

#### Part 2

> **Directions:** Work with your team to develop text messages to persuade teens to stay safe during physical activity. Write at least 2 tips or pieces of advice for 3 of these categories. Be sure your messages have accurate information and would appeal to your peers.

## Categories

**Drinking enough water**

_____

_____

_____

**Reducing injuries**

_____

_____

_____

**Climate/weather**

_____

_____

_____

**Warming up/cooling down**

_____

_____

_____

**Safety gear**

_____

_____

_____

_____

> ## Self-Check
> ☐ I explained why it's important to drink water when being physically active.
> ☐ I explained at least 3 ways to reduce the risk of injuries during sports and other activities.
> ☐ I described at least 3 ways to respond to climate- or weather-related conditions during physical activity.
> ☐ I explained the importance of warming up before and cooling down after physical activity.
> ☐ I listed at least 3 activities that require safety equipment and explained how it protects you.
> ☐ I wrote advice for someone just beginning physical activity.
> ☐ We wrote tips for 3 of the safety categories.

# Information Hunt

**Directions:** Write down your nutrition or physical activity question. Then research the answer and prepare for your presentation. Be sure to use at least 2 reliable sources and write them down.

▶ **My question:**

_____
_____
_____

▶ **My sources:**

(Be sure to list the author, name of the article, name of the journal or book and year of publication. For websites, give the complete address, year updated and author/agency responsible for the content.)

_____
_____
_____
_____

**How I know these sources are reliable:**

_____
_____
_____
_____

**Use the space below to organize notes from your sources and plan your presentation.**

_____
_____
_____
_____
_____
_____
_____
_____
_____

## Self-Check

☐ I identified at least 2 reliable sources of information and explained how I know they are reliable.

☐ I used my sources to gather information and wrote notes to answer my question.

☐ I organized and planned my presentation.

# Influence Analysis

**Directions:** Work with your group to describe or give an example of at least 1 way each of these factors could influence your choices around healthy eating or physical activity. Label each influence as positive (+) or negative (–). Be prepared to explain your answers.

| Influencing Factor | Example of how it can influence | Positive (+) Negative (–) |
|---|---|---|
| Family | | |
| Friends/Peers | | |
| Culture | | |
| School | | |
| Community | | |
| Media | | |
| Technology | | |
| Personal beliefs | | |
| Government recommendations | | |

**HEALTH** *Smart.* High School

# Influences on My Eating or Physical Activity Behaviors

> **Directions:** Describe 4 positive influences on your eating or physical activity behaviors and explain how each one supports you. Describe 4 negative influences on your eating or physical activity behaviors and explain 1 specific strategy for overcoming or resisting each of them. Then answer the questions.

▶ **Positive Influence** | **How It Supports Me**

1. _____ | _____
2. _____ | _____
3. _____ | _____
4. _____ | _____

▶ **Negative Influence** | **Strategy for Overcoming It**

1. _____ | _____
2. _____ | _____
3. _____ | _____
4. _____ | _____

**①** Which positive influence gives you the strongest support for eating healthy and being physically active? Why?

_____

_____

_____

_____

_____

**②** Which negative influence do you most often need to overcome in order to eat healthy and be active? Do you think the strategy you've described will work? Why or why not?

_____

_____

_____

_____

_____

_____

_____

> ### Self-Check
> ☐ I listed 4 positive influences and described how each supports me.
> ☐ I listed 4 negative influences and described a strategy for overcoming each.
> ☐ I wrote which positive influence gives me the strongest support and described why.
> ☐ I wrote which negative influence I most often need to overcome and told why I think the strategy I described will work or not.

# Body Image Assessment

**Directions:** Choose 5 body parts from the list. Write a sentence or two describing what you like about each of these parts of your body.

## ▶ Part 1

### Body Parts

- Hair
- Skin
- Hands
- Nose
- Ears
- Eyes
- Neck
- Height
- Legs
- Teeth
- Feet
- Posture
- Eyelashes
- Fingernails
- Face
- Lips
- Muscle tone
- Arms
- Waist
- Shoulders

**Body Part** _____

**What I Like About It**

_____

_____

**Body Part** _____

**What I Like About It**

_____

_____

**Body Part** _____

**What I Like About It**

_____

_____

**Body Part** _____

**What I Like About It**

_____

_____

**Body Part** _____

**What I Like About It**

_____

_____

_____

# Body Image Assessment

*(continued)*

## ▶ Part 2

**(1)** How would you explain the difference between a positive and negative body image? Tell about at least 2 differences, and give an example of each one.

_____

_____

_____

_____

_____

**(2)** What influences your body image? Name at least 2 influences and describe how they affect your view of your body either positively or negatively.

_____

_____

_____

_____

_____

_____

_____

**(3)** What are at least 3 ways you can support a positive body image for yourself and others?

_____

_____

_____

_____

_____

_____

**(4)** What are at least 2 things you could do to improve your body image?

_____

_____

_____

_____

_____

### Self-Check

☐ I explained at least 2 differences between a positive and a negative body image and gave an example of each one.

☐ I listed at least 2 influences on my body image and described how they affect my view either positively or negatively.

☐ I listed at least 3 ways I can support a positive body image for myself and others.

☐ I wrote 2 things I could do to improve my body image.

# Weight Loss
# How Much Do You Really Know?

**Myth:** **Fad diets work for permanent weight loss.**

**Fact:** Fad diets are not the best ways to lose weight and keep it off. Diets often promise to help you lose a lot of weight quickly, or tell you to cut out certain foods to lose weight. Although you may lose weight at first you may not get all the nutrients that your body needs. Many people quickly get tired of diets and regain the lost weight.

Research suggests that losing 1/2 to 2 pounds a week by eating better and exercising more is the best way to lose weight and keep it off.

**Myth:** **Skipping meals is a good way to lose weight.**

**Fact:** Your body needs a certain amount of calories and nutrients each day in order to work properly. Most people who skip meals during the day make up for those missing calories by snacking or eating more at the next meal. Studies show that people who skip breakfast tend to be heavier than those who eat a nutritious breakfast.

A healthier way to lose weight is to eat many small meals throughout the day that include a variety of nutritious, low-fat and low-calorie foods.

**Myth:** **Weight loss pills are safe and effective.**

**Fact:** Even though weight loss pills are sold at health food stores, grocery stores and online, they are not safe or effective. These products are not regulated by the government and the labels are not always accurate. Some types of over-the-counter weight loss pills can increase the risk of stroke, high blood pressure, seizures and even death. These pills also do not help people permanently lose weight. The best way to maintain a healthy weight is to eat healthy and to get plenty of physical activity and exercise.

**Myth:** **Eating after 8 p.m. causes weight gain.**

**Fact:** It doesn't matter what time of day you eat—it's how much you eat during the whole day and how much exercise you get that make you gain or lose weight. If you want to have a snack before bedtime, make sure that you first think about how many calories you have already eaten that day.

**Myth:** **Certain foods, such as grapefruit, celery or cabbage soup, can burn fat and make you lose weight.**

**Fact:** No foods can burn fat. The best way to lose weight is to cut back on the number of calories you eat and be more physically active.

# Weight Loss
## How Much Do You Really Know? *(continued)*

**Myth:** **Natural or herbal weight-loss products are safe and effective.**

**Fact:** A product that claims to be "natural" or "herbal" isn't necessarily safe. These products are not usually tested by scientists to prove that they're safe or that they work.

Some herbal and natural products may be unsafe for people with certain medical conditions.

**Myth:** **Eating red meat is bad for your health and will make it harder to lose weight.**

**Fact:** Red meat, pork, chicken and fish contain some saturated fat and cholesterol. But they also have nutrients that are important for good health, like protein, iron and zinc.

Eating lean meat in small amounts can be part of a healthy diet.

**Myth:** **Starches are fattening and should be limited when you are trying to lose weight.**

**Fact:** Rice, pasta, bread, beans and some vegetables (such as potatoes, squash, turnips, beets and carrots) are rich in complex carbohydrates (also called starch). Carbohydrates are an important source of energy.

Foods high in starch can become high in fat and calories when they are made with rich sauces or high-fat toppings. Avoid high-fat toppings and choose foods high in fiber, such as whole grains, beans and peas.

**Myth:** **High-protein/low-carbohydrate diets are a healthy way to lose weight.**

**Fact:** If the diet allows foods high in fat, it can raise blood cholesterol levels, which increases a person's risk of heart disease and certain cancers.

This is not a healthy way to lose weight! High-protein/low-carbohydrate diets may cause rapid weight loss—but most of it is water weight and lean muscle mass—not fat. You lose water because your kidneys try to get rid of the excess waste products of protein and fat, called *ketones,* that your body makes. This can overwork the kidneys and cause dehydration, headaches, nausea, fatigue and dizziness.

Following a reduced-calorie diet that's well balanced between carbohydrates, proteins and fats will help you lose weight without hurting your body.

**Myth:** **"Going vegetarian" means you are sure to lose weight and be healthier.**

**Fact:** Vegetarian diets can be healthy because they are often lower in saturated fat and cholesterol and higher in fiber. Choosing a vegetarian diet with a low fat content can be helpful for weight loss. But vegetarians—like nonvegetarians—can also make poor food choices, such as eating large amounts of junk (nutritionally empty) foods.

# Ask the Expert!

**Directions:** Use what you know about healthy and safe weight loss to answer these letters. Be sure to explain whether the way to lose weight talked about in the letter is healthy or unhealthy and why. Provide clear advice to the letter writers about the importance of healthy food choices and physical activity in losing weight or maintaining a healthy weight.

Dear Expert,

I just started this high-protein, low-carbohydrate diet. It's been really hard not to eat any bread or fruit, but I've already lost 2 pounds. My friend thinks what I'm doing is unhealthy. But it seems to be working, so what's so unhealthy about it?

Sincerely,
Nothing But Protein

(1) Dear Nothing But Protein,

_____

_____

_____

_____

_____

_____

_____

_____

_____

_____

_____

Dear Expert,

I saw this ad for some weight-loss pills on the Internet. The website had statements from people saying how much weight they lost using the pills, and how fast it was. Is there any reason I shouldn't try it? The pills are expensive, but they'll give you a free 2-week supply if you order 3 bottles.

Sincerely,
Magic Pills

(2) Dear Magic Pills,

_____

_____

_____

_____

_____

_____

_____

_____

_____

_____

_____

_____

# Ask the Expert! *(continued)*

Dear Expert,

My sister wants to lose weight, so she's gone on this cabbage soup diet. All she eats is cabbage soup, plus some vegetables at dinner. She says she's lost a bunch of weight, but I think she's kidding herself. Could something bad happen to her if she keeps eating this way? What should I tell her about other ways to lose weight?

> Sincerely,
> Sick of Soup

**(3)** Dear Sick of Soup,

_____
_____
_____
_____
_____
_____
_____
_____
_____
_____
_____
_____

---

Dear Expert,

I've tried all kinds of diets to lose weight, but nothing seemed to work. Lately, I've been really trying to eat healthy foods in the right amounts. I'm feeling good about that, but I'm still not losing weight. What else can I do that will still be healthy for me?

> Sincerely,
> What's Missing

**(4)** Dear What's Missing,

_____
_____
_____
_____
_____
_____
_____
_____
_____
_____
_____
_____

---

## Self-Check

☐ I wrote answers to all 4 letters and explained why each weight loss strategy is safe or risky.

☐ I explained healthy ways to manage weight.

# Ways to Help a Friend

## If you're concerned about a friend, don't keep it to yourself. Your friend's health may be in danger.

■ Not eating enough can make someone feel cold, tired or moody. It can cause dry hair and skin. For girls it can interfere with the menstrual cycle and weaken bones.

■ Vomiting can damage the throat and teeth, and using laxatives too often can hurt the intestines.

■ Binge eating can lead to obesity or being overweight.

## ▶ Here are some things to do:

■ **In a calm, caring way, tell your friend what you've seen or heard.** Use I-statements. Here are some suggestions:

- "I'm worried about you because you haven't eaten lunch this week."

- "I heard you talking about taking laxatives (or diet pills) and that scares me."

- "Are you OK? Were you vomiting after lunch? I'm concerned about you."

■ **Listen carefully to what your friend says.** Your friend might feel ashamed, scared or unimportant. Feeling out of control also is common. Not eating or eating too much may be your friend's way of coping with problems.

Your friend might deny it. It's very common for people with eating disorders to say there's nothing wrong. Your friend might get angry, ask you not to tell or promise not to do it anymore.

■ **Tell your friend you care and want to help.** Encourage your friend to talk to an adult to get help. Offer to go along for support.

Tell your friend that you don't want to keep your concern a secret. Your friend's health might be in danger.

■ **Tell an adult about your concern.** Consider talking to your parents or your friend's parents, a teacher, or the school nurse or counselor. Tell someone who can get help for your friend. It's not "tattling" or "ratting" if you're worried about your friend's health.

Here's what you could say:

- "I'm worried about _____ because I (saw her or him throw up on purpose/take a laxative/take diet pills/throw away her or his lunch)."

- "I'm concerned about _____ because (she or he always complains about being too fat/seems so sad/says she or he never can do anything right)."

**You're doing the right thing!** You can't solve your friend's problems, but you can share your concerns and tell an adult so your friend can get professional help if needed. **Eating disorders must be diagnosed and treated by a health care professional.**

# Preventing Food-Borne Illnesses

More than 48 million illnesses and 6,000 deaths result each year from food-borne illnesses. Most of these illnesses are preventable. Teens prepare food at home or at work in food service jobs. So it's important to know the facts.

## ▶ Causes

Food-borne illnesses are caused by viruses, bacteria and parasites found in a wide range of foods. Foods commonly linked with illness include:

- Unpasteurized fruit and vegetable juices
- Raw or undercooked eggs, chicken, meat, and fish
- Lettuce, sprouts or other leafy vegetables that are contaminated in the field
- Foods with cream fillings

## ▶ Symptoms

Symptoms of food-borne illnesses may occur as early as 30 minutes after eating contaminated food, but typically don't develop for several hours or days. Symptoms usually last only a day or two, but in some cases can last up to 10 days. Symptoms include:

- Diarrhea
- Fever
- Severe exhaustion
- Abdominal cramping
- Headache

## ▶ What to Do

- Wash your hands before you eat, before you prepare food, after meals and after using the restroom. To wash hands effectively, scrub them with soap for 20 seconds, rinse in warm water, and dry with a paper towel.
- Check expiration dates on food labels.
- Wash fresh fruits and vegetables thoroughly.
- Avoid using cutting boards made of soft, porous materials.
- Never taste food to see if it's spoiled. If unsure, throw it away.
- Always use clean utensils, counter tops and cutting boards to prepare food. Wash them between different foods.
- Don't cut meat, chicken or fish on the same board as fruits or vegetables. This helps avoid cross-contamination, or the transmission of germs from one type of food to another.
- Don't sample cookie dough before cooking.
- Keep hot foods hot and cold foods cold. Hot foods should be kept at 135°F or above, and cold foods at 41°F or below.
- Clean the blade of a can opener after each use.
- Cook meat, fish and chicken thoroughly.
- Don't consume foods from cans or jars that are damaged (e.g., rusted, cracked or bloated).

Nutrition & Physical Activity

# Food-Borne Illness Detective

**Directions:** Read the following news stories. Use what you've learned to identify likely causes of the illness and describe at least 2 strategies that could have prevented the food poisoning in each case.

**One man** is dead and 22 have been treated for salmonella poisoning after eating at a local food fair. At one booth raw hamburger was placed on a pancake, which was then rolled up and deep-fried. Health officials revealed yesterday that a 75-year-old man and his wife took the rolls home, refrigerated them and ate them for lunch the following day. The man was found dead. His wife is recovering at the local hospital. The health department has confirmed that 21 other people tested positive for salmonella. The others who became ill also ate at the food fair.

**Food that most likely caused the food-borne illness:** _____

_____

**Food safety strategies that could have prevented the illness:** _____

_____

**Investigators** from the local health department have confirmed 5 more cases of hepatitis A. There have been 25 other cases in the past 2 weeks. Today's findings bring the total number of people infected with hepatitis A to 30. Health officials believe that the first cases are linked to an infected worker at a local restaurant. A cook with hepatitis A is believed to have spread the virus. Investigators are in the process of tracing all 30 cases back to the restaurant.

**Foods that most likely caused the food-borne illness:** _____

_____

**Food safety strategies that could have prevented the illness:** _____

_____

**An entire family** is recovering in the local hospital after being treated for *E. coli* bacteria infection. Yesterday all 5 family members were admitted to the hospital after becoming violently ill, with symptoms including vomiting and diarrhea. Health authorities isolated *E. coli* bacteria in specimens obtained from the family members and in leftover chicken in the family's refrigerator.

**Food that most likely caused the food-borne illness:** _____

_____

**Food safety strategies that could have prevented the illness:** _____

_____

## Self-Check

☐ I identified the likely cause of illness in all 3 stories.

☐ I described at least 2 strategies that could have prevented the illness in each case.

HEALTH*Smart.* High School